Group Education and Facilitation Skills in Healthcare Settings

A Successful Diabetes Handbook

Rosie Walker and Jill Rodgers

Published by SD Publications, Successful Diabetes, PO Box 819, Northampton NN4 4AG.

ISBN 978-1-4476-6087-3

Contents

Contents (continued)

Contents (continued)

About Us

Successful Diabetes is an independent company run by health professionals who are education specialists. It provides products and services to benefit those working or living with diabetes and other long term conditions.

It offers a wide range of products including books and ebooks, workshops and website resources such as recipes and practical tips along with news and comment on key issues as they arise.

Rosie Walker and Jill Rodgers are the Directors of Successful Diabetes. They have a detailed knowledge and vast experience in facilitating learning groups of all sizes and for many different purposes, especially in diabetes education, communication and consultation skills and group processes themselves. They are committed to the learner centred approach upon which this book is based and which it describes in detail. In addition, many of the examples throughout the book are taken from their real life experiences, learning and reflections.

Acknowledgement

We would like to thank Marti Funnell RN CDE for contributing her facilitator story to this book.

Marti is the diabetes education lead at the Michigan Diabetes Research and Training Center (MDRTC) in the University of Michigan, USA. She has provided us with inspiration over many years.

Introduction

Welcome to your essential guide to providing wonderfully successful health related education courses or workshops. It's specially designed to help you to promote more effective learning among group members, for example in group education sessions, focus groups or discussion forums. The philosophy of participants being involved and creating the environment for using effective learning techniques are central themes. It's full of useful, practical information and resources to make everything run smoothly and it is equally useful whether you are just getting started or you already have experience but wish to further develop your skills.

Section one is all about advance planning, one of the most important aspects of successful group education, as it influences everything that happens during your session. For example, it is no good having exceptional practical skills to encourage participation if nobody turns up to the sessions! Planning includes focusing on practical aspects such as seating layout, refreshments or whether there will be room for participants to be comfortable in small groups. Section one covers all these aspects and more.

Section two focuses on what influences effective learning and looks in detail at the essential facilitating skills to enable successful achievement of learning outcomes, for example, how to ensure everyone participates, nobody dominates and you keep to time. It also looks at barriers to learning that might arise in group education and gives practical solutions about how to avoid or overcome them.

Both sections include a range of evaluation tools, as well as many tried and tested tips, examples, checklists and ideas you can put into practice. Throughout the book there are also many ideas and suggestions for maximizing interaction and participation. The book ends with a range of true-life, unique facilitator stories to illustrate the important messages covered throughout the book.

This book gives examples from education sessions about diabetes and other healthcare settings, but you may find the planning and facilitation skills described also transfer to other activities in your work or life. For example, when running work team meetings or away days. They can also help at home when you need to organise a celebratory event, have a crowd of teenagers all talking at once in your house, or even when family discussions get heated round the dinner table!

All in all, it's a mine of useful information for all types of group education and situations. We hope you enjoy reading it, finding the most useful sections for you at different times and putting its contents into practice!

Rosie Walker and Jill Rodgers

Section 1

Planning and Preparing for Group Education

Chapter 1: Planning Your Programme

"Failing to plan means planning to fail" is a common expression and it applies well to group education. No matter how useful the content and information discussed in your sessions, any programme will be completely wasted if there is inadequate planning to ensure everything works well on the day. This chapter looks at planning the actual programme for your sessions, from identifying your initial learning outcomes down to the last detail, so that your participants get the maximum benefit and learning from the session.

Planning your learning outcomes

The most important part of programme planning is, perhaps surprisingly, the end! What outcomes are you aiming to achieve, and what learning do you want your participants to take away from the session? By starting here, you are much more likely to deliver an effective session. So, what exactly do you want people to be able to do, explain, describe at the end of your programme? It can be quite difficult to achieve, for example do you just want someone to understand something new, or do you want them to be able to apply that to a given situation?

Once you have identified your learning outcomes, not only will they help you to shape your programme, but it is also useful to share these with participants so that they know what to expect from the session, and also what won't be included. It is common for people to arrive at sessions with unrealistic expectations, and then even if the session is excellent in other ways, they can be disappointed or confused if their expectations are not met, as one of our facilitator stories in chapter seven shows. This in turn can result in poor evaluation of the session, leaving you as a facilitator feeling that your time and efforts have been wasted. It also means that your participants may be less likely to attend any future sessions.

Types of outcomes

It's easy to think of learning outcomes as simply those relating to the content of the education. Whilst these are important, they are not the only type of outcome which needs to be considered. Apart from outcomes focused around the content, other outcomes that need to be considered are the experience the participants have, what changes they make in their behaviour as a result of the programme, and also the educational process itself. The table below identifies examples of each type of outcome discussed here.

Type of outcome	Example
Content or information	Participants will be able to explain what healthy eating means
The experience that participants have	Participants will have had the opportunity of sharing ways of managing diabetes during illness with other participants
Changes in behaviour	Participants will have identified at least two healthy lifestyle actions to try before the next session
Educational process	Participants will have had the opportunity to ask questions during the session

Once you have identified the specific outcomes you want, it becomes much easier to develop your programme, as the outcomes become the framework for the order of activities and ensures that you do not forget to include all aspects of learning.

Outcomes can also form the basis for evaluation or audit, so considering them carefully at the start of the planning process will ensure you have meaningful and comprehensive material for review at the end of your group education event.

Structuring your programme and activities

The next step is to structure your programme according to the time you have available. This means creating a framework to include time for introductions, for the main content to be delivered in a meaningful way, for evaluations and farewells, and for adequate breaks.

From a content perspective, your programme will obviously need to include the topics you wish to cover, but it is important not to overfill the time with content, even if you feel that there are many important messages to convey. Too much content will result in less learning, as your participants need time to process the information they are receiving. It can be more useful to think about how people can explore the areas you wish to cover themselves, for example by experimenting between sessions and bringing their learning to the next session.

For the content that you decide to include, the methods you use to deliver it are important. These include what activities you will use, what materials you need for the participants, and how you will explain the activities to the participants. The programme also needs to allow time for some form of feedback from the activities, which can be in small groups or as a whole group, because giving feedback is a way of participants processing the information they have been working with and also a way they can share and reflect on their thoughts and ideas together.

As well as the activities, it's vital that you build sufficient time into the programme for introductions and farewells. These are important learning occasions as well as social necessities. Introductions help people to feel at ease and part of the group, as well as ensuring that everyone has a chance to speak early in the session, and farewells help people to know that the session has ended and perhaps also to summarise what they have learned. More information on the ways these can be achieved successfully without taking up too much time can be found in chapter five.

Breaks and refreshments are also important. Sessions of more than two hours will need to have break times built in, to ensure participants are comfortable and refreshed, which enhances their learning.

Paying attention to these aspects, which put people at ease and ensure they are comfortable, shows respect for the participants, helps them feel valued, and ensures that their physical and social needs are being considered. If introductions, farewells and refreshment times are squeezed out in favour of more content, perhaps because time is considered to be too short to include them, people are less likely to learn effectively and may also be confused about what is happening. This diverts their attention and concentration from the purpose of the session and its activities.

Evaluation is also important, and can take many forms. Whatever method you use, time will be needed towards the end of the programme to achieve this. In general, allowing time for people to complete evaluations in person rather than asking for a postal return will give you a greater response rate, so finding time on the day is very worthwhile. There are many different types of evaluation in addition to filling in evaluation forms, which are described in detail in chapter six.

Successful Diabetes Tip

To enable your participants to learn effectively, you need to use a variety of methods to present information, particularly those where people interact with each other, use materials and resources relevant to the session topic, and have time to reflect and discuss what they are learning. These methods are more effective than lectures or Powerpoint presentations, and will result in greater retention of information and personally meaningful learning.

Demonstration programme structure

This demonstration programme layout, showing some hypothetical content, shows you one way to ensure that you pay attention to all the important aspects of planning your group session, including who will run each session and what resources you will need. You would obviously need to fill in the timings and specific activities for your sessions.

Time	Activity	Name of Facilitator	Resources and notes
	Registration and pre-session activities		List of names, Refreshments
	Welcome, introductions, explain programme and facilities		Programme for each participant
	Activity 1		Paper and pens for each participant
	Activity 2		Flipchart sheets and pens for each small group
	Feedback from activity 2		Sticky tack for flipchart sheets
	Refreshment break		
	Activity 3		Information cards – 1 set per group
	Feedback from activity 3		
	Evaluation and questionnaire completion		Relevant forms
	Farewells		Next session information letter

Preparing for invited speakers

During your group sessions, you may wish to invite a guest presenter or facilitator. It's important to ensure that this visitor to your session is prepared and informed about the following:

* The date and time of the session and their section of it
* The venue address, parking and transport arrangements
* Your contact details on the day they are attending
* The outcomes that the session should provide
* What resources will be available as standard and what they may need to provide themselves
* The break times and refreshment arrangements

It is useful if you can find out from your visitor if they have any particular requirements in relation to the layout of the room, seating arrangements, equipment or personal needs. Also, if they will be providing handouts for their sessions, they may require some printing or photocopying to be done on your part.

Exchanging telephone numbers, including mobile numbers in case you need to be in touch on the day of the visit. means you can get in touch if either of you have any concerns. It is also useful to confirm all the arrangements and details already mentioned by letter or email, particularly if you are planning the session well in advance, so that any misunderstandings can be avoided and your session runs smoothly. A quick reminder email or phone call close to the event can also help.

During the visitor's session, it is helpful if you can be there so that you can deal with any issues that arise, for example if equipment needs to be re-arranged or a participant needs help unexpectedly. This means that the visitor can concentrate on delivering their session without any additional worries.

If your visitor is to be paid for their session, you will need to plan how payment will be made and organise for prompt payment. Your visitor may need to supply an invoice, or there may be a standard payment arrangement already in place. Whatever the payment arrangements, discuss them in advance and make sure they are transparent. It is also a good idea to arrange a note of thanks to them, and if appropriate a token of appreciation. This is likely to result in them enjoying working with you and also being happy to return if asked in the future.

Successful Diabetes Tip

Ensure any invited speakers have all the details of the venue and equipment available and knows exactly what time slot they have and the outcomes for their session. Exchanging contact details with them for the day of the session will ensure you can easily get in touch if any last minute needs arise.

Chapter 2: Participants and Their Needs

Your participants are the most important people in the room, so it is important to think of anything that will make the session easier for them to attend and participate in. Also, participants who are upset or feel uncomfortable with any aspect of your session will tend to learn less and also are unlikely to attend future sessions! This chapter discusses the ways that you can ensure your participants feel comfortable and able to interact fully during your sessions.

Arranging the venue

Whatever venue you use, you need to ensure that there will be enough room for the number of people you expect to attend. You will also need room to carry out the various activities. For example, if you are planning to have small group work (which we would recommend), you may need extra rooms or a large main room for people to be comfortable to do this.

You will also need enough room for equipment and resources. These might include flip charts, slide projector and laptop, and space for reference materials and refreshments. It can be useful to also have space on the walls to display flip charts or other resources that develop from the group activities.

When using an outside venue, be prepared for every eventuality. Check and double check with the room organiser that everything you need is in place, and make sure you have their contact details on the day of your event. On the day, bring with you equipment and resources that you know you will need, for example, flip chart paper and pens, sticky tack, scissors and sticky notes, and printed copies of any slides. This will mean that you are prepared and can run your programme even if the venue does not provide what you expected.

It is essential to consider health and safety and disability needs in respect of access, toilet facilities and ease of movement during the session. For example, ask yourself: could a person with restricted mobility easily move around (or be helped to move around) the room or rooms to participate in activities? Is the room a long way away from the refreshment area, which might mean you need longer in the programme for participants to get there and back in the breaks? For everyone coming, you need to consider ease of access, car parking and public transport links, as lack of attention to these aspects can result in participants being stressed and upset on arrival. This then results in extra time being needed for their stress to reduce, and will also affect their ability to concentrate and learn.

At the venue, you will need to ensure that participants can find the room easily. You can achieve this either by putting up signs or by having someone to welcome and direct people as they enter the building.

If you are hiring or borrowing a venue for your session, a visit in advance is highly recommended as there may be a difference in how you and the person you have booked with perceive its suitability (see facilitator stories, chapter seven). It is particularly important if any of the participants have special needs or disabilities that need to be catered for. A visit will give you the chance to plan the room layout in relation to your activities, to assess access and parking facilities and to ask about or work out how and where refreshments will be served.

Successful Diabetes Tip

If a venue (even your own) is not suitable or adaptable to the needs of your programme, participants are unlikely to be comfortable, which will affect their learning. It is better to adjust your programme, the number of participants or find another venue than it is to hope for the best!

Number of participants

You might be wrestling with the all-important question about the ideal number of participants in a group. The answer is that it depends on:

a) What you are hoping to achieve in your session, and

b) How many facilitators you have available and how confident they feel in their role.

In relation to a), you might invite fewer people to a session which involves learning a particular skill, for example in diabetes education, learning to perform blood glucose monitoring, injecting insulin or carbohydrate counting. For a discussion session aimed at participants sharing their most effective ways of managing diabetes day to day, larger numbers could be accommodated.

For b), a larger number of facilitators can mean that you could cope with greater numbers, with some activities carried out as a whole group and participants being separated into smaller groups in different rooms for parts of the session.

Whatever the size of the group, if you are less experienced as a facilitator, or you want to try a new approach such as introducing greater participation, a smaller group of people might be easier to manage until you become more confident.

If you are already confident about using a participatory approach, this can be achieved successfully whatever size of group you have, whether it is a large conference audience or a small workshop with 6 to 10 people. The skills needed to achieve this, and the different ways that can be used to ensure an interactive approach whatever your group size, are described in detail in Section 2 of this book.

The table below outlines some of the pros and cons of larger and smaller group sizes.

	Advantages	Disadvantages
Small groups	* Can use a smaller venue * More personal – people can get to know everyone * Less time needed for introductions and activity feedback * Less confident participants can more easily contribute	* Possibly less experience to share * There will be less variety of people to work with in small groups * Clashes of opinion or personality are more obvious
Large groups	* Plenty of experience to share * Participants can get to know a wide range of people * More varied evaluation as it comes from many perspectives	* More time is needed for participatory activities * A larger venue and resources may be more costly * You may not notice those who are less able or willing to participate

Here are a few practical examples in relation to participant numbers:

* If you want to hold whole group discussions for part of the session, no more than 20 participants per facilitator will make sure everyone gets a chance to contribute.

* If your session is concerned mainly with learning practical skills with two facilitators, a group of 12 might be more appropriate.

* If a session is mostly devoted to in-depth whole group discussion, then having no more than 10 people per facilitator will ensure there is enough experience to discuss, but also that everyone gets a chance to speak to the others without feeling overwhelmed by the group size.

Another factor that can influence how many participants to invite is the length of time the session will last. Feedback from activities tends to take longer if you have more participants, although feedback methods can be tailored to the time available. Also, remember that if you have invited participants to bring someone with them, this could potentially double the number of people attending your session.

When using a participatory approach, it is important to remember that the focus is on the participants experience and desired outcomes, recognising that people learn a great deal from others in similar situations to themselves. Too few people being present could mean there are less experiences and views to share, which may be disappointing for them.

Whatever number of participants you decide upon, it is important that the venue and space available for the session activities is sufficient to accommodate them all comfortably.

Successful Diabetes Tip

The number of participants that you invite is rarely the number who arrive on the day! Expect up to 10% of your participants to be unable to attend on the day, often due to events beyond their control. On the other hand, people may arrive without prior confirmation. You can limit the number of non-attendees, or unexpected attendees, by carefully wording invitations, managing their expectations, and following up your initial invitation in good time.

Invitations and information prior to the session

Personalised invitations containing clear information about timings, what to expect and what to bring are essential. When attending group sessions, people are often anxious that they will be singled out in some way, made to speak up in front of everyone else, or 'put on the spot'. These worries often arise from previous negative experiences, so reassurance about what to expect in the invitation information can be very helpful and encourage attendance.

Your participants also need information about the venue, how to get there, and where to go on arrival. If they are expected to bring or pay for refreshments or a meal, this also needs to be explained. In some cases, you may like to invite them to bring someone else with them to the session, to learn about the topic, but also to provide them with personal support and encouragement.

The clearer you can be in the invitation information, the more successful your session is likely to be, as all participants will start off with a shared understanding of what will happen and why.

Successful Diabetes Tip

People are often put off attending a group session because of their negative beliefs about what might happen, based on previous experiences. Invitations that address these beliefs and offer reassuring information are likely to result in greater attendance.

Refreshments

Refreshments are essential to a successful group session. If it is a whole day or evening session, you will need to make arrangements for lunch or supper. You can provide food, people can bring their own, or people can be asked to use a nearby restaurant or canteen. If your participants need to bring or pay for their meal or other refreshments they must know this in advance. It is important to consider whether the cost of meals, however small you think it will be, might be too much for some participants to pay. It is also important to check that the type of food provided by caterers or in local facilities will be suitable for all the participants.

As a minimum and even for short sessions, drinking water should be available in the room you are using for the whole of the session. This will enable people to be comfortable. It is ideal if you can provide hot drinks and some snacks as well at break times.

It's important to stick closely to the timings of the refreshment breaks and meals during your session, to make sure everyone is comfortable. If the session is for people with diabetes, they may have adjusted their medication or other eating and drinking to suit the timings on your programme or in your invitation letter. Other practical reasons are that people may have made arrangements to make phone calls or meet personal needs based on the timings on the programme. Delays or changes can cause inconvenience and anxiety, which will inhibit people's concentration and their ability to participate in the session.

Creating a safe and comfortable physical and psychological environment

Your participants will be able to learn more effectively if they feel comfortable both physically and psychologically. From a physical point of view, attention to the type of seating available, the arrangement of seats and proximity of participants to each other are all important considerations.

Seats should be soft and not too low, and provide enough support but not be too rigid and uncomfortable. The most effective room layout if you are running an interactive session is a semi circle of chairs only, with no tables in front of them. Tables create a sense of territory and act as barriers to communication. They are also reminiscent of formal meetings, which produce particular expectations of the session, which may not be accurate in relation to the session you are actually providing.

It's important to have enough space between seats, and slightly larger gaps near to the entrance and exits so people can join and leave the group easily. If you know that someone is attending who uses a wheelchair or walking aid, or who has vision or hearing problems, consider what might be the best position for them and reserve that space for them. When they arrive, you can check with them that the position is suitable for their needs.

From a psychological perspective, a warm welcome on arrival and some introduction to the room and seating and refreshments can help a great deal. In an education session, particularly one which is health related, encouraging participants to bring someone else with them is also important. This means that no-one has to walk into a room full of strangers on their own, which can cause a high level of anxiety, and it also means that someone close to them can experience the session and its content, too.

People will feel psychologically comfortable in a group situation if they feel that they are among people in similar situations to themselves, that they know what to expect and that they will be treated with respect. Paying attention to these aspects will enable your participants to take part in the session effectively. The specific facilitation skills described in section two of this book describe how this can be done.

Chapter 3: Troubleshooting and Evaluation

This chapter provides information on how you can plan ahead for any circumstance to work out how it can either be avoided or how it can be dealt with on the day, and also how you can go about evaluating your sessions.

Planning for success

"The best way to predict the future is to invent it", so the saying goes, and a useful way to predict a successful group session is to take into account anything that could go wrong and ensure you consider how to prevent it happening or deal with it if it should arise. We call this aspect of planning the 'What if...? scenario' and here's how it is done. Take a piece of paper and divide it into three columns, and insert the titles shown below in each of the columns. Then complete the sheet with all your potential scenarios. Carrying out this activity with colleagues is likely to result in more 'what ifs' being identified, and thereby help you to be more prepared for anything that could happen.

What if...?	What could I do if it happens?	How could I prevent it happening?
Only half the people I was expecting arrive at the session	* Run the session as planned but with fewer people * Check the invitation was clear enough * Contact people who didn't come to find out what stopped them, and whether it was personal or organisational issues	* Make sure the invitation is very clear about the details and what to expect * Arrange to contact people the day before to check they are coming and if someone is coming with them * Add a reply slip to my letter of invitation, including their contact number on the day

Constructive evaluation following the session

Once you have run your session, you will have an idea of how effective your planning and preparation was. A useful way of capturing this is to constructively evaluate the session, using the following questions:

* What went well?
* What went less well?
* What could I do differently next time?
* How did the participants respond?

You can apply these questions to the session overall, to each particular section or to the participants' evaluations. This approach will help you plan the next session to be even more successful than the last! Ideally, you should constructively evaluate every session at the earliest chance you have, and use your evaluation to adapt and make changes. But beware of making constant changes based on single comments, it is more productive to take an overall view, for example if one person disliked an activity but all others were positive. If you record your reflections in a diary, notebook or computer document, together with any changes you make to the session, you can refresh your memory of any important aspects the next time you are preparing to run a similar session.

Successful Diabetes Tip

Keep a paper or computerised diary or log of your group sessions so that you can refer to previous entries and reflections when you are planning your next similar session, to avoid repeating aspects that didn't go well.

Checklist for planning a successful group session

This checklist summarises all the planning and preparation issues covered in section one of this book. You could use this format to help get you started with your group sessions.

What needs to be done	Who is to do this, and by when	Date of completion, comments
Decide the title of the session		
Identify all types of outcomes		
Decide on numbers (including partners where appropriate)		
Decide on methods of delivery and what activities to use		
Decide on timings for each activity, including feedback		
Write programme, including introductions, refreshments, evaluation and farewells		
Decide on the room arrangement and check this can be achieved		
Identify what could go wrong and make plans to deal with it		
Invite participants and any speakers, collate replies, exchange contact details		
Follow up non-responders to check if they will be attending		
Double check the venue arrangements a few days before the session		
Collect all the equipment and resources you need for the session, check they work		
Constructively evaluate the session and decide on any changes needed for the next session		

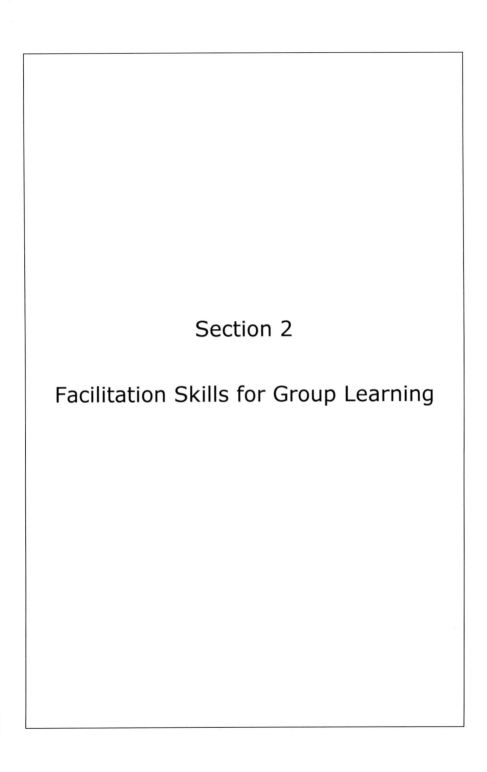

Section 2

Facilitation Skills for Group Learning

Chapter 4: Learning and Facilitation

One factor that has consistently been shown to make a difference to how much people retain from any education session is the approach of the facilitator. This chapter discusses the different approaches that can be used together with their relevant successes, and describes what good facilitation is all about.

Approaches to teaching and learning

There are a number of possible approaches to education and the terminology and methodology used varies accordingly. One main distinction is between a 'teacher-centred' and a 'learner-centred' approach.

In the first, as a teacher, you are considered to have all the necessary expertise, knowledge and experience in relation to the subject, and you would tend to use didactic or 'telling' methods to impart this to the learners. So you might give lectures, talks or demonstrations, set tasks which are given marks or grades according to performance, and test the outcomes of the session by how much knowledge has been transferred, for example with a fact-based test, questionnaire or quiz.

By contrast, if you use a learner-centred approach, you would start from the perspective that learners have experience, expertise and knowledge, which is then built upon during the education session. This approach has been proven to be more successful in helping people learn.

The methods you use in a learner-centred approach will be more participatory and interactive, and your role is much more that of facilitator, enabling the participants to share their thoughts with each other to enable new learning to emerge. You might provide the answers to any gaps in knowledge, but this will be in response to any that cannot be addressed by the learners themselves and which they identify as necessary, rather than the answers you feel you need or have to provide.

Importantly in a learner-centred environment, you discard the assumption that knowledge resides within an individual, and particularly that the facilitator or teacher has more knowledge than anyone else in the room. Instead, you take the view that knowledge is distributed throughout the group, including the facilitator or teacher. So for example, a question raised by a participant would be directed back at the group to find the answer, instead of being answered directly by the facilitator. This approach is consistent with the belief that learners are a source of useful and appropriate information and experience, which can be shared, and also that their participation will enhance their learning.

In a learner-centred approach, the social and cultural context is important, as well as the academic aspects. This means that you would pay particular attention to the environment in which the session takes place and to the relationships between the participants. In formal terms, this is known as a social constructivist approach and is the approach used and recommended by Successful Diabetes.

A more teacher-centred approach is the traditional way that education has been provided, and remains dominant in education in general, not only in educational institutions such as universities. This approach can be seen in a great deal of health related education such as diabetes structured education, although many courses are beginning to encourage participants' contributions more and value the role of the participant as much as that of the teacher or group leader.

Despite the teacher-centred approach still being used in some areas or situation, there is a large and increasing body of evidence showing that a learner-centred approach in both adults and children results in personally meaningful learning taking place. Also, in group education, that participants often learn much more than the original purpose the session was set up for, which in turn is more enjoyable and stimulating. In the words of Jerome Bruner, the American educationalist, "knowing is a process, not a product."

What's special about learning in groups?

When people who have something in common learn together, they enjoy and learn from methods and activities which enable them to meet each other, share and compare their knowledge and questions, and reflect on their experiences. This 'vicarious experience' as it is known, where people learn from other people's experiences as well as their own, is a powerful force for increasing confidence to take action, known as self-efficacy. In health-related education, and particularly in diabetes education, learning in groups has been shown to give participants new insights, and stimulates them to make positive changes in some areas of their diabetes self care.

One of the reasons that learning is a group is so effective is that people can identify with others in similar situations, or even when the situations are different there are still common themes. This can provide psychological and emotional reassurance to a person that their thoughts, ideas and behaviours are neither unusual nor wrong. It also helps them to feel that they are not the only one struggling or using particular coping strategies in a situation, and thereby reduces feelings of guilt or inadequacy.

The evidence for learning effectively in groups is not confined to people with diabetes or any other condition, but applies equally to any group learning, including health professionals learning together. The experience of learning from each other in a group is often informally reported in evaluations as 'networking' or 'hearing about how others deal with situations'. In formal terms, this effect is referred to as peer learning, informal learning or situational learning.

What is facilitation?

The word facilitation literally means 'to make easy'. Pure facilitation is concerned with the process of a group's learning, rather than the detailed content, although in practice in many education settings, a facilitator is often engaged in both. For example, if you were a diabetes specialist nurse facilitating group education to commence insulin therapy, you might be involved in both giving information about insulin or insulin delivery devices as well as creating a comfortable and interactive environment. Hence the term 'facilitator of learning' encompasses all these aspects, as it is possible in any teaching role to also be an effective facilitator.

Facilitating learning in groups

Facilitating learning in groups is both an art and a science. It is an art because it involves you working with people who have come together for a particular purpose, but who also bring their individual thoughts, feelings and beliefs, which will impact on the learning experience. So therefore every group experience will be different because of the difference in participants and in the topics and direction the group goes in.

It is also a science because good facilitation requires you to have some knowledge and understanding both of how people behave in group situations and of factors which enable or inhibit learning in adults. This will help to ensure it is a successful experience for all participants and achieves the stated outcomes.

To facilitate groups successfully, a number of skills are required which are not necessarily taught in healthcare situations or training, so additional education of people who will be involved in education in healthcare is essential. The next chapter discusses those skills in detail.

Chapter 5: Facilitation skills in detail

This chapter provides a step by step guide of how to facilitate groups, from the time the participants arrive to the time that they leave. It is divided into subsections so that you can easily identify each component, and provides in-depth information both of what is effective in terms of participants' comfort and their interaction, and examples of how to put it into practice.

Greeting participants on arrival, and registration

As well as ensuring participants are directed to the specific room in which the session is to be held, it is essential to welcome them when they arrive in the room. A personal approach, asking their name and the name of anyone they have brought with them (if relevant), and a word or two about their experience of getting there, can make people feel very comfortable. This is particularly valuable if they have had difficulties with delays or parking for example, to give them a chance to vent any negative emotions, which might influence their attention during the session.

Welcoming on arrival can also include brief introductions to other people, so they can chat informally rather than sitting in a silent room. Light background music can help when people arrive, as it offers a distraction and makes any silence less noticeable.

A registration process helps you to keep accurate records of attendees, which can be valuable data for audit purposes as well as for personal review. A table where people sign in and collect any information packs, resources or reference lists they need is helpful.

You may also have resources for people to look at before the session starts, with clarity about what can be taken away and clear labelling of materials that should not be removed. Participants can also be invited to share their contact details if they wish. It should be clear how these details will be used, and participants should sign to give their consent for their details to be shared or distributed.

Starting the session – welcome and introductions

Your opening remarks need to include a warm welcome, thanks to the participants for attending and introduction of the facilitators and any other people present, such as observers or support staff. The outline of the programme for the session should also be given verbally. This needs to be followed quickly by the opportunity for participants to introduce themselves, to each other as well as to you. You can do this in a number of ways, depending on the time available and the size of the group.

One way is to work your way around the room, asking each person to briefly say their name and where they live or work (as relevant), and what are their hopes for the session. This can be time consuming if there are a large number of people, so putting a time limit on each person's contribution (such as 30 seconds or a minute) might be necessary.

With larger numbers or limited time, introductions can be more relaxed and effective if people are invited to introduce themselves in twos or threes to each other, and continue to introduce themselves to new people throughout the session, rather than to the whole group.

Whichever way you choose, some form of verbal introductions is vital, as the earlier that someone contributes in a session, the more likely it is they will contribute again. Name badges or stickers help enormously to remind everyone (and you) who's who, and gives you the chance to learn what people prefer to be called (sometimes not their given name). Being able to be called by their name enhances the personal nature of the session for participants, leading to more comfort and hence more learning.

Ground rules

Ground rules or boundaries are also essential. With them in place, things rarely go wrong, but without them, chaos can reign, as everyone has a different understanding of what behaviour or contribution is acceptable.

The traditional approach is to set ground rules for a group, but a more successful approach is to enable participants to set their own ground rules. This enhances ownership and willingness to abide by the rules set. Only rules to which everyone feels they can agree should be used. Examples of common ground rules include:

✳ Sticking to set timings

✳ Not interrupting each other when speaking

✳ Having mobile phones switched off or in silent mode

✳ All questions are welcomed

The process of agreeing ground rules will give you an insight into what your participants think is important and what will help them feel comfortable in order to learn. If time is tight, or if participants find it difficult to think of what to suggest, a way of including ground rules is to offer a ready-made list of a few, and ask the participants to talk to each other in pairs or small groups. This gives them the chance to briefly discuss which of the ground rules they agree with and what others they would like to add to the group. It is important that ground rules added by participants are also agreed by the rest of the group.This process offers added bonuses of people having the chance to talk with each other, and of feeling that they are involved in the session very early on.

Successful Diabetes Tip

Always include introductions and ground rules in your session. They are often omitted when time appears to be in short supply, but this results in participants' discomfort and confusion and hence reduced capacity to learn. Not having ground rules also makes it more likely that there will be unequal participation within the group.

Promoting and encouraging participation and interaction

As mentioned earlier, if your participants speak early in the session, this increases the likelihood of them contributing again. Hence, giving every participant the chance to speak during the introductions and welcoming is an important skill, whether it is in small groups or as part of the larger group.

The more your participants feel they are contributing and having their learning needs met during the session, the more they will be able to learn. Ways to ensure that everyone gets the chance to contribute and participate in activities include:

* Enabling people to talk in pairs and small groups at regular intervals

* Inviting people who haven't yet said anything to contribute to a whole group discussion

* Designing activities that specifically ask for a contribution from each member of the group

* Monitoring a group or small group discussion for participation

* Inviting questions, both verbally and written

* Asking for feedback from group sessions by different individuals

Successful Diabetes Tip

To make sure everyone has the chance to contribute from small groups, invite verbal feedback from someone other than the one who has been making notes or writing on a flip chart during the group discussions. If time allows, you could ask for a short comment from everyone in the group.

The value of small group interaction

Your participants will learn as much, if not more, from each other as they will from you and from the information being presented at the session. This situated learning, as it is known, is more likely to result in changes in behaviour, because the participants are being influenced by others that they see as similar to themselves. This vicarious experience has been shown to be an important factor in increasing a person's confidence to take action, known as self-efficacy. So the more opportunities you can create for participation and interaction, the more learning can take place that is personally meaningful to participants and that will result in changes in the way they self-care.

You can check how 'interaction friendly' your programme is by looking at each session and assessing how much you and your participants are interacting or contributing at that moment. The greater amount of each session where you are the person being active, the less participatory your session is. The more your sessions are broken into activities undertaken by the participants, the more interactive it is. The higher the percentage of activity the better, and as you increase the amount of time that your participants are predominantly interacting or contributing, you are well on your way to a programme that will be useful to your participants' learning. If you find that you are the most active person in a session, consider how you might organise discussion groups or sharing of ideas in some other way to cover the given topic.

One useful way of promoting interaction is to organise the session into a series of activities designed to meet the outcomes of the session, which participants undertake in pairs or small groups. Each group may do a similar activity or you may choose to have several different activities representing different aspects of the topic.

You can mix the groups throughout the session, so your participants get the chance to work with a variety of other people and share views and experiences. It is important to ensure that people understand the activity and its purpose, and to support the small groups as they work, so that everyone contributes fairly and the activity is completed in the time allocated.

Ways to mix participants in small groups

The purpose of creating small groups and to mix these groups from time to time throughout the session is to allow everyone to have some input into discussion, to avoid long periods of whole group discussion where people will often disengage, and to promote peer learning. It is also useful to keep the discussions fresh and to create an active environment, particularly to promote concentration which can be especially important after meals and breaks.

It is quicker and more effective for the facilitator to create groups and to tell them where to work in the room, rather than to expect participants to do this themselves. Asking people to form groups themselves often brings back memories of 'picking teams' when at school, or promotes participants who know each other staying together rather than mixing with others, which limits opportunities for sharing knowledge and experience. It also is a distraction from the activity.

The size and make-up of small groups should be led by the specific activity. Where participation is needed from every member, groups should be kept to no more than three or four people. Regarding make-up of groups, there are times when an activity will be more suited to people who come from a similar area, who work together or who have attended the session together, for example when making a joint action plan. At other times, a mixture of different participants may be needed, for example when the activity demands sharing experiences from a variety of perspectives. If a series of linked activities is planned, where one activity is naturally an extension of the one before, then keeping participants in the same groups throughout this period would be suitable. For separate activities, it can be beneficial to change the make-up of the groups more often.

Dividing people into groups can be a lively and enjoyable experience, which aids participants' memories of the session. It is important at this stage to be open in your thoughts about letting people work with others, rather than trying to 'fix' groups, unless there is a specific reason)related to your outcomes) why people should or should not work together. A key skill is to be neutral about the topics or ways that you choose to divide people into groups. See the facilitator story 'Respect your participants' in chapter seven for an example of why this is important.

There are many different ways of mixing participants into different groups, for example:

* Give each participant round the room a number according to how many groups you want. For example, if you want six groups, number people from one to six and repeat this as many times as you need to. Ask all the participants with the same number to work together.

* Create sets from a pack of playing cards according to the number of groups you want to create – for example three picture cards of the same suit, four cards with the number seven on, or six diamonds, then shuffle the cards and distribute them. Invite all the participants with the same set to work together.

* Invite participants to stand in a line or circle according to some order, for example where their birthday is in the year, in alphabetical order of first names or surnames, wearing similar colour clothes or types of jewellery, then divide people according to the size of groups that you want.

Explaining learning activities

Participants will get even more out of pairs or small group work if the activity is explained to them well. In order to be able to do this, you need to be clear yourself what you expect the outcome of the activity to be, for example:

* A list of items to which everyone has contributed
* A drawing representing a small groups view of a particular situation
* Items on a list sorted into the most and least important, or their relevance and irrelevance to the topic

You may need to give your participants a demonstration or an example of what you are expecting them to achieve, and allow them to ask questions for clarity, before they start, as lack of understanding of the activity is likely to lead to a variation of responses and potentially less learning related to the session's intended outcomes.

Explaining the context of an activity is also helpful. Your participants will not appreciate being given things to do that don't seem to be relevant to their learning. If you can't explain the relevance of the activity to the learning outcomes, it may not be the best activity to include.

When explaining an activity to participants, it is also helpful to explain whether all groups will be undertaking the same activity, and also the format of any feedback which will be taken, so they will be prepared for this. For example, if you wish the feedback from one activity to be further developed in the next, explaining this will aid the psychological comfort of your participants.

Successful Diabetes Tip

When you design an activity for your participants, try explaining it to a colleague or family member to see if they can understand what they need to do and why. Refine your explanation until it is clear and use this version in your session.

Learning activities for interaction and participation

Activities that are most likely to promote processing and remembering information, known as deep learning, include any that involve active engagement with the content and discussion about it. Activities which represent examples of authentic or 'real life' situations for the learners are particularly useful for deep learning. On the other hand, activities that involve passive listening, single out individuals, involve trick questions or promote guessing games about the correct answer, are likely to result in less learning and more resistance.

The following are some examples of how collaborative learning in small groups can be achieved:

* 'Warm up' activities: arranging cards containing words and phrases or pictures into categories; putting topics in order of importance to be addressed; discussing words, phrases or mental images that come to mind in relation to a particular topic. This enables participants to become engaged with the topic in a light way, preparing for more detailed information later.

* Arranging topic cards on flipcharts into categories, for example 'true', 'false' or 'don't know'. This enables the group members to learn from each other, but also identifies gaps in knowledge for all members.

* Fill in the blanks – either from a set of suggested responses or by participants discussing and agreeing the most appropriate word or phrase to insert from their own experience. This promotes discussion among group members about their experiences and enables them to share their knowledge.

* Looking at materials relevant to the topic, eg books, leaflets, documents or reports, and assess their use or application in given situations. This enables participants to become familiar with relevant materials but also to analyse their value.

* Arranging or rating features or statements about a particular aspect of the topic. This encourages group members to consider a topic in detail.

* Creating a drawing or diagram, based on current knowledge. This can be a welcome relief from writing all the time, but also helps to show different ways of understanding a topic.

* Undertaking a quiz or 'bingo' type game. This enables factual knowledge to be shared and clarified.

* Make up a poem, song, recipe or rap from key information. This helps to distil important information, release creativity among group members and helps in memorising information.

* Creating questions about a particular topic. This helps group members to answer each other's questions but also to identify those to which everyone needs the answer.

Keeping attention focused on the activity

This skill complements the skill of explaining the activity or discussion topic, so that your participants know exactly what they need to do or discuss. If you include a specific ground rule about keeping on track, you can refer back to this in order to keep the participants focused on their specific task.

In discussion groups, if participants or small groups become sidetracked into other discussions, you can decide whether to intervene or not. Some sidetracks are valuable discussions even if they were not the original topic. If discussions do become sidetracked, you can point out that discussions have veered away, and ask the group if they wish to continue with their current topic or return to the original one, taking a vote if necessary.

In relation to activities, a lot depends on whether the group have completed the activity and are now talking more generally, or if they have become engrossed in other conversations and are not completing the activity. If your activities are designed for a specific purpose (as is ideal), this will be important, as not completing it will mean the loss of valuable feedback and perhaps not being able to undertake the next, linked activity. So reminding the group of the task, and encouraging them to complete it, is essential. You might need to explain the purpose of the activity again to ensure the group understands, or remind them of the time they have to complete it.

If the participants become bored, sleepy or feel stressed by their situation, their attention will wander, so building variety and mobility into your programme activities and methods will ensure that participants' attention remains focused.

Taking feedback

Your participants will be keen and willing to report back on their discussions, more so if they have been alerted to the need for this in the preparation for the activity. Feedback enables the whole group to hear each other's experiences, and can also be used for you to gain an insight of participants' understanding of the issues under discussion, plus an opportunity for both you and the participants to clarify any misunderstandings or erroneous beliefs.

The skill in taking feedback, and for it to fulfill its purpose, is to enable all groups to contribute without any one group or person dominating, and without leaving one group without anything to add. This can be achieved by taking one or two points of feedback from each group at a time, or asking them to give a timed overview of their answers rather than each individual detail (and keeping strictly to this timing!). Other ways of organising feedback in a timely manner, while maintaining full involvement of all participants, are:

✳ To ask pairs or small groups to join up with other groups to share the outcomes of their discussions and report back as a bigger group

✳ For groups to fix their work (eg flip chart sheets) onto the walls and then to 'tour' each other's outcomes, adding new ideas or comments where relevant

✳ To create a voting system where groups show a card or item with their response to a particular aspect of their discussions

The way you take feedback will depend on the topic under discussion, the purpose of the activity and the number of participants. Remember that for some activities, no feedback is necessary, for example if the activity is directed at participants' personal thoughts or feelings, or if it is linked directly to the next activity. It is always worth considering if feedback is necessary and what its purpose is, rather than having a standard format.

Successful Diabetes Tip

When taking feedback, thanking the participants for their contribution is an important aspect. For many people, speaking in front of even a small group takes great courage, so respectful acknowledgement of their efforts may influence their confidence to speak again.

Handling questions

Questions are an important way in which your participants will make sense of the information discussed and help them to retain it. Welcoming questions is an important facilitation skill, as is involving the whole group in answering them, rather than simply answering the questions yourself. In this way, your participants get to contribute, share their knowledge and learn from each other as well as from you.

Using questions to respond to queries arising from the group, such as 'what have been other people's experiences?', 'has anyone else come across that?' or 'what do others think about that?' can all help to elicit people's views and thoughts and produce a richer learning experience.

Your expertise and knowledge is important, but should be used as an addition or completion of what the participants know, rather than because you feel it is important to point out. If you feel a strong urge to add information, thinking about how you can pose this as a question to the group or incorporate it in an activity is more likely to result in useful learning. Also, by adding relevant information in response to unanswered questions, or to clarify people's ideas, you can increase their chances of retaining the information and also build their confidence to act upon it. It is also important to check back with the person who originally raised a question to ensure they have gained a satisfactory answer.

Some questions might arise to which no-one, including you, know the answer. In this situation, the group's attention can be directed towards ways in which the answer might be found, for example by participants consulting reference material or others who might be able to offer an answer. This can be a very valuable exercise, where your participants gain important problem-solving and coping skills, as well as new ways of finding information that they may not have considered before. You may feel you have to take on the responsibility of finding out every answer for them, but this may be less productive in terms of their learning. Also, you may not need to answer or seek to answer every question at the time it arises, but you could make a note and allow some time for covering these before the end of the session.

Inviting questions at regular intervals is useful, to enable your participants to reflect on what they are learning. You may like to have 'question time-outs' where pairs consider what questions they have at this point in the session. This has the advantage of not putting individuals on the spot, and also gives another opportunity to share their thoughts. Having a ground rule relating to questions will help to keep them relevant and timely and enable people to feel comfortable asking. If you have a series of activities planned in order to gradually unfold some information, you can let the group know this and can keep a note of the questions that arise, so that you can address any that remain unanswered at the end.

Another opportunity for questions is by creating a 'question board' where your participants can anonymously place questions on a sticky note, or write them directly, so they can raise their questions without having to ask in front of everyone. If this method is used, it is important to check the board at intervals and address the questions.

If you use group questions as a means of eliciting information or understanding from your group, for example 'who has heard of xxx?' 'who knows what xxx means?', alerting them in advance of your reason for asking will ensure they do not feel interrogated, 'put on the spot' or that they are playing a guessing game, all of which can inhibit learning.

Successful Diabetes Tip

If you let your participants know what to expect in relation to questions, this will enable you to keep the programme running to time and meet your outcomes. It will also enable the participants to feel comfortable enough to ask questions and to respond to your questions.

Using non-verbal communication

"A man may be silent but he chatters endlessly with his fingertips" said Sigmund Freud, and it is true that non-verbal communication can influence both you and your participants as much as what you say out loud. Being a skilled facilitator includes being aware of which non-verbal signals promote or hinder successful learning.

Understanding the impact of your non-verbal behaviour will enable you to utilise non-verbal signals effectively. Here are a few examples:

* Eye contact: Making eye contact with your participants as you are speaking, explaining activities or taking feedback can make the group feel listened to and acknowledged. However, too intense or prolonged eye contact, or focusing on one person, can make people feel uncomfortable.

* Facial expressions: many facial expressions are unconscious and include movements of eyebrows and expressions that indicate puzzlement, approval, disapproval or surprise. Your participants will be aware of these, even if you are not, so spending some time raising your awareness of your own facial expressions, either by yourself or through feedback from a colleague or friend or even your group, might be useful.

* Smiling: This indicates warmth and encouragement when it is spontaneous, but is likely to be unnerving if it seems false or fixed.

* Standing and sitting: Altering your position will influence the energy levels in the room. Moving from a standing to a sitting position creates equality between you and the group (if they are already sitting) and also give 'the floor' to the person or people who are contributing or feeding back at that time. If you are working with a co-facilitator, sitting when they are speaking also directs the participants' attention to the speaker. On the other hand, you can use a move from a sitting to a standing position to indicate an end to a current discussion or debate, or a moving on to a new topic, or a break.

* Hand movements: Opening your hands towards your participants indicates your focus on them, inviting them to

contribute. A gentle raise of your hand and arm can show that you would like to gain their attention. A raise of your hand from your wrist towards someone or a group who are engrossed in their own contribution or conversation can bring this to a close.

* Moving around the room: Walking whilst talking can create a sense of energy and enthusiasm, although too much movement can be distracting if you wish the participants to act upon or retain the information under discussion. On the other hand, walking quietly around groups who are engaged in an activity can create a feeling of security.

* Purposeful movements: Walking directly towards an individual can have two contrasting effects. Firstly, it can have the negative impact of making someone feel nervous or uncertain of what is going to happen, so needs to be undertaken with care in order to avoid this. Secondly, it can be an extremely useful skill to use when someone is dominating the discussions or is difficult to interrupt. Often people are unaware they are doing this when they are engrossed in their topic, and so do not respond to more gentle cues such as the hand movement described above. In this case, walking directly towards them and standing near to them, perhaps even touching their shoulder or arm gently, while saying clearly that you need to interrupt them can be very effective in bringing the contribution to a close and moving on.

Successful Diabetes Tip

If your participants do not seem to be taking in or working with the information you are providing, consider whether your non verbal communication could be confusing them in some way.

Identifying non-verbal communication of participants

As well as being aware of your own non-verbal communication, you need to be able to respond to that of the participants in your group. This non-verbal communication can take many forms, including:

* Yawning, stretching, eyes drooping, or fidgeting: these usually indicate a loss of concentration, perhaps because the session has exceeded their attention span (usually not more than 20 minutes without a break or being able to participate). Another reason might be because the session is just after a meal, when physiological processes interfere with people's ability to concentrate for a time. A further reason might be if the participant has a low level of interest in that particular topic.

* Eyes watering or glistening, blowing the nose, head bowing: these can show that someone is feeling upset by something, which may be the content of the session or perhaps discussions that have taken place.

* Vigorous nodding or shaking of the head: these can show the person is very engaged in the topic, but may hold strong views about it and be indicating agreement or disagreement with the content under discussion and perhaps a desire to contribute.

* Opening of body posture (relaxing) or closing of body posture (arms folded, focused inwards): this can show a change in attitude to the topic being discussed or to something another participant is saying or doing.

Once you identify a non-verbal cue from your participants, the skill is to respond to it as soon as possible. This does not have to be a direct response to the person, but can be a general comment that indicates your understanding of the situation. Examples of the type of comment you could make are: "I can see a few people are looking a bit restless/tired, shall we have a quick break?" or "I think now is a good time to take questions" or "sometimes people feel quite emotional when this topic is discussed". Another way of acknowledging individual non-verbal communication you have noticed is by mentioning it to the individual at a suitable moment outside the group, telling them what you saw and checking with them how they are feeling. This personal acknowledgement can be greatly valued by participants, whether they were conscious of their actions or not.

> ### Successful Diabetes Tip
>
> If you feel anxious, tired or upset while you are facilitating a session, you may be responding unconsciously to the feelings among your participants. Check if their non verbal communication is trying to tell you something!

Dealing with difficulties arising in groups

From time to time, tensions may arise in a group. These can be due to confusion about the purpose and expectations of the group, personal difficulties that participants are reminded of in relation to the programme content, emotional reactions to the content, or personality clashes within the group. Any tensions that arise can lead to disagreements or arguments between the participants. They can also lead altering the way that people participate in your activities, either by aggressively dominating any discussion or by withdrawing from participating, which might be accompanied by closed body language. Emotions may run high, from people feeling angry, upset, or embarrassed.

An overall technical term for tensions that arise is 'resistance' and it can get in the way of the learning outcomes of your session being achieved. A key facilitation skill is to be able to recognise and deal with forms of resistance. Ways you can do this include:

* Inviting questions and ensuring clarify about the purpose and programme of the group session at the outset
* Ensuring that agreed ground rules are adhered to

* Letting the group know that part of your role as facilitator is to deal with any tensions that arise and to remind participants of their ground rules

* Acknowledging that there is a disagreement and inviting participants to compromise or leave the disagreement behind in order to continue the programme for everyone's benefit

* Periodically inviting comments from the whole group about how they are feeling and reminding them that they can note down issues or questions anonymously

* Allowing the group members to deal with issues themselves and to help each other to start with, and only intervening if they are not resolved

* Tactfully acknowledging strong emotions such as fear, anger or aggression and diffusing them through group discussion

> ### Successful Diabetes Tip
> Change the make-up of small groups and pairs regularly, so anyone who dominates or distracts others does not spend all their time with one group of people. This avoids frustrations which will then affect people's learning.

Using silence

"Sometimes silence is the best answer" is one of the Dalai Lama's mantras, and effective use of silence is one of the best ways to elicit information from a group. As too much silence can create a sense of awkwardness, the skill in using it is to know just how long to let a silence continue.

Commonly, very little time is left after a question is asked of participants before the facilitator fills the gap by speaking themselves, but you need to leave long enough after a discussion or question for people to collect their thoughts and think about their answers. A silence will rarely last more than about 10 seconds, but staying silent even for that long can be difficult, particularly if you are not used to it! Practising ways of resisting the urge to move on too quickly following a question will give your participants a chance to think about their response, which will in turn facilitate their learning as they process and consider information.

During moments of silence, you can use the time to be aware of your participants' non-verbal behaviour as well as your own. You can also use non-verbal communication to invite response, for example by looking at people, smiling warmly, or gently walking towards the participants or among groups.

Successful Diabetes Tip

To resist the urge to speak yourself during a silence designed to enable participants to respond, counting slowly in your head from one to 10, or reciting a familiar phrase or rhyme (silently to yourself!), can be useful distractions.

Timekeeping

Your programme will have timings for the individual sections, and it is likely that the whole session will also be time limited. This may be planned to fit in with your own timing constraints, but it is also important to remember that your participants have many things going on in their lives and will be expecting the session to start and finish on time, as they will probably have made arrangements for what they will be doing when the session finishes. Keeping strictly to the start and finish times shows respect for your participants and reduces the risk of them being anxious about time, or having to leave before the programme is complete, both of which will distract them and so limit their learning opportunity.

Checking timings in the introductory session, and reminding your participants of the finish time and length of the session, can be useful to ensure there are no misunderstandings among the group.

This also gives people a chance to say if they need to leave early or if they have particular needs for breaks at a certain time.

Keeping each activity and feedback to time is a key facilitation skill, so having a clock to hand in case there is not one in the room you are using can be helpful. When you have asked groups to work on an activity, alerting them a few minutes before their time is due to end enables them to complete their discussions on time and also helps to keep them focused on the activity.

Successful Diabetes Tip

People often appreciate sessions finishing a little earlier than planned – an unexpected surprise – so when planning your programme, leaving a little more time for sessions than you think you are going to use can enable this to happen.

Ending the session – farewells

Endings are as important as beginnings. They are a time for acknowledgement of the participants' contributions and time, a summing up of what has been learned and a signpost to future sessions or events. As with introductions, giving everyone the opportunity to say something, or write something anonymously, is helpful. This process can also contribute to evaluations.

When a group has enjoyed its time together and found the experience valuable, the group members may want to exchange contact details with each other, so if you build in time for this, as well as for evaluation forms to be completed, your participants will feel their experience is complete.

If time is short or the session has overrun, endings and farewells are often overlooked. But, however brief it is, it is important to include some form of ending to the session that the group members can participate in. This consolidates their learning and shows respect and acknowledgement of their presence and contribution.

Ways of ending a session include:

* A 'reflective round', where each person has the opportunity to briefly sum up their experience at the session. It is not essential for everyone to say something, but having the chance to is important.

* Inviting small groups or pairs to discuss and complete the sentence 'today I have learned…' on a flipchart on the wall.

* Inviting your participants to give themselves a round of applause.

* With agreement from all, taking a group photograph to share or be viewed on an electronic central place.

Successful Diabetes Tip

Distribute certificates of attendance, or small souvenirs related to the topic of the day, to your participants. They will serve as an ending of the session, mementos of their experience, and will act as later reminders of what they have learned.

Chapter 6: Making It Successful

This chapter discusses what can go wrong in your sessions and what solutions you might find to deal with this, both in terms of planning ahead to avoid the situation happening, and in dealing with situations that arise during the session. It also identifies ways of evaluating the session so that you can continually make improvements ready for the next time it runs.

Troubleshooting

Even with the best planning and preparation and to the most seasoned and experienced facilitator, things can and do go wrong, as some of the facilitator stories in chapter seven show. Also, if you are moving from a teacher-centred to a more learner-centred approach, you may have worries about situations that might arise.

 The key to dealing with whatever happens is to plan in advance as much as possible, even for situations that seem very unlikely to happen. Working with your colleagues will mean that you are more likely to identify a large number of things that would prevent your session running smoothly on the day. If you work out in advance how you can deal with issues that might arise, you will be much better equipped to be able to cope if the situation occurs in reality.

On the next page is a format that you could use to analyse your concerns. The table shows some common concerns that might occur with the organisation of group sessions and some approaches you could take.

Situation	How it could be handled
Venue is double booked or locked	Phone the organiser. Consult confirmation arrangements. Explain what is happening to participants and ask for their patience.
Non-working projector or password-protected computer	Consult onsite staff or organisers. Consider how you can present the information differently. Give participants an activity to do while it is being investigated.
No participants turn up	Check you have the right arrangements. Wait for a time. Identify anything that might have held them up, for example traffic problems or a venue with the same name.
The room layout does not suit your group's purpose	Be specific about what you want in your booking agreement. Arrive early enough to give you time to rearrange the room if necessary. If the room cannot be rearranged, identify how you can carry out your activities with the current layout.
Refreshments are unsuitable or insufficient	Talk to the provider or organiser. Ask them to provide a substitute if possible. Consult your booking arrangements. If necessary, provide different refreshments, for example from local shops.

This is not a complete list, and you may be able to think of many more things that could go wrong, or even some that have gone wrong in the past! By using this format, you will have a ready-made list of what to do in almost every eventuality, and will be able to deal with it much better on the day without raising your stress levels too much. If you get flustered by things that go wrong, this can have an impact on the way you deliver your sessions and, as a consequence, on how much participants get out if it.

It is also worth considering what might happen within the session as you are facilitating your group. Again, some examples of these are shown in the table below, together with solutions that are known to be successful.

Situation	How it could be handled
Participants will not contribute	Divide into small groups. Invite each person by name to contribute. Hold the silence. Ask open questions.
A participant won't stop talking	Ask groups to ensure that everyone gets a chance to speak. Change small group composition regularly to avoid domination. In a large group, specifically ask those who haven't already spoken to say something. Walk towards the high contributor, stand nearby and say "can I just stop you for a moment, to let some others say what they think, too".
Participants don't take part in an activity and digress from the topic	Re-state the activity and its purpose. State how much time there is left. Consider if the topic is too boring or too much time is allocated to it.
Participants become angry, aggressive or tearful	Accept their feelings. Ask them if they can explain what is making them angry or aggressive or upset. Allow the group to comment. Do not tolerate violence or threats – invite them to leave if they continue.
I don't know the answer to a question	Ask the group if anyone knows the answer. Consider together the ways the answer could be found. Agree how the answer can be found out for the next session if necessary.

Evaluation

Evaluation is an essential tool for successful learning. Without it, you have no means of knowing the effect of your chosen methods, content or activities. Considering evaluation as integral to the success of your programme will help you design a method to give you valuable information.

Evaluation can be formative, which means ongoing during the session, at intervals during the session, or at the end of specific activities. It can also be summative, at the end of the session, set of sessions or individual activities. Ideally, both methods should be used, as the purpose of evaluation is to obtain feedback, which you can then act upon to refine your programme for the next time it runs.

The more sensitive your evaluation methods are, and the more aligned to the outcomes you have set, the more useful will be the information that you obtain. For example, if your learning outcomes include your participants creating an action plan for a health-related behaviour change, then your evaluation method must identify whether this has happened. In this example, you might choose to ask the participants to state their action plan, to answer yes or no regarding whether they have created one, or to rate the likelihood that they will. So a good place to start when creating an evaluation tool for your session or activities is by looking at the learning outcomes.

As well as the learning outcomes, you can evaluate other aspects of your session, for example the degree of participation your participants experienced, their enjoyment of the activities, or the venue and facilities.

The most common form of evaluation tool is the evaluation form, typically given out and completed by participants at the end of the session or set of sessions. Sometimes there isn't time for the form to be completed, or participants have to complete it in a rush, making the resulting information less useful. An alternative is to draw your participants' attention to the form at the start of the session, and invite them to complete it at intervals during the session, or remind them to capture their thoughts on the form as the session progresses.

An evaluation form can invite participants to rate their opinion on a scale, either with numbers (eg from 0-10) or words (eg from poor to excellent), or freely write their comments. An evaluation form combining both these methods will give you more insight into their experiences, and be more useful when reflecting and assessing the session's success.

There are other evaluation methods, which you can use as well as (or instead of) an evaluation form. These include:

✳ Supplying each participant with a set of sticky notes and asking them to write their responses to a particular activity or topic and to place their sticky note on a flipchart

✳ Write a sentence on a flipchart and ask people to complete it in their own words, eg 'at the moment I'm feeling…' or 'from this activity, I've learned…'

✳ Asking participants to compete a chart with four squares, for example labeled 'most useful', 'least useful', 'suggestions for change' and 'what I enjoyed most'

Chapter 7: Facilitator stories

This chapter provides insight into some real situations where less than ideal planning resulted in education sessions being run in unsuitable venues without adequate facilities. Each story describes how the facilitators coped on the day and what they learned as a result!

Being prepared

I was once invited to facilitate a group education session for health professionals. The venue had been organised by someone else and I was assured it would have a projector, laptop and flip chart and the room would be suitable for the 12 participants. When I arrived, I found there was no equipment to present the slides and the room was very small and dark, with only six uncomfortable plastic chairs in it! The venue did not have a record of what had been booked in terms of equipment or numbers, there were no other rooms available, and the organiser, who I was expecting to attend the session, did not arrive.

How did I deal with it? Three participants did not arrive, so there was just enough space for those who attended. I was been able to bring into the room some chairs from the corridor outside, so that everyone had a seat. I had brought with me a printed copy of my small number of slides, which the venue allowed me to photocopy for each participant. We viewed these instead of projecting the slides. All the other activities I had planned were interactive and I had brought the resources for them, so the programme went to plan, although very uncomfortably at times for all of us.

What did I learn? To gain confirmation in writing with the organiser that the venue is suitable for the number of participants, the equipment I need will be in the venue and whom to contact if all is not in place. To continue to carry printed copies of slides if I am using them, and to have a contingency plan for any activity for which I need resources from the venue or organiser.

Unexpected guests

I was invited to run a workshop for 23 participants. The number of participants and their names were confirmed to me the day before the event, so I took enough materials for this number plus a couple of extra copies. On arrival, I set up the room for 23 people. The participants started arriving… and arriving… until 28 people were sitting in the room!

How did I deal with it? It was very difficult! it was not just a question of the copies of materials, which needed to be shared, but it was also tricky to run some of the activities and hold the required feedback in the time allowed, because all these take longer with greater numbers. I had to cut down the planned feedback time for each group, in order to ensure everyone got a chance to participate.

What did I learn? When planning a programme for numbers above 20 people, build in the possibility that more might arrive and have a plan for how each activity and feedback can be adapted for more people. Also, at a time close to the event, to ask the organisers whether they plan to check whether non-responders are planning to come along.

Expectations dashed

At the start of a session I was running on the topic of using the empowerment approach in diabetes consultations, I first stated the title of the workshop to the participants and gave an overview of the programme for the day. One participant raised their hand and asked at what time the session on insulin devices would be held. There was no session on insulin devices included in my programme, but it became clear that this participant had come specifically to learn about them and so left the workshop.

On another occasion, I was invited to run a workshop on consultation and communication skills for a particular approach, but the flyer that the organisers sent out only advertised it as how to complete the locally used computer system templates, which was but a small part of the session.

How did I deal with it? I explained the programme to the participants and offered them the opportunity to leave if they felt the session was not going to meet their needs. In the first scenario, the participant wanting information on insulin devices chose to leave the session. In the second scenario, the participants were somewhat surprised but also relieved, as it turned out to be more interesting than an IT workshop, but this could easily not have been the case!

What did I learn? To ask workshop organisers about the information they have sent to the participants in advance of the workshop, to ensure their expectations are in line with what will be delivered. Also, to give clear information to organisers about what the session I am delivering will and will not contain.

Managing expectations

I was running an education session for people with diabetes, about how to be more effective in providing service user representation to local planning groups. At the start of the session, as usual, I asked each individual to write on a sticky note (anonymously) what they specifically wanted to get out of the session. When I reviewed the sticky notes, three of them had written that they wanted to know more about diabetes in one way or another, including what insulins were available and about foot complications. The session was not an education session about diabetes itself, and I became concerned that people would feel their needs hadn't been met if I didn't cover all the things they'd asked for.

How did I deal with it? Well, I read out the content of all the sticky notes to the participants, and commented on the three that wanted to know about diabetes: "this workshop isn't specifically to teach you about diabetes, but most of the people in this room have got diabetes and there is a wealth of information you can tap into. So use this opportunity to talk to each other and find out the things you want to know, and also come and talk to me and the Diabetes UK representative during the breaks to help you find ways of getting the information you need".

At the end of the day, I personally hadn't been asked any questions about diabetes. I asked people to remove their own sticky notes if they have got what they had stated they wanted. The three sticky notes about diabetes were all removed.

What did I learn? This experience reinforced to me that we don't have to be the 'experts' and give everyone what they say they want, but that we can often find ways of people getting the learning they want in different ways. It also reminded me what a fantastic resource any group can be, how important 'meeting, sharing and comparing' is, and that people often learn more from each other than from the person at the front of the room, and I now make that explicit in every workshop I run.

The process is your responsibility

I remember turning up at a session to find that the venue was quite unsuitable – the space I had asked for wasn't available, the seats were in fixed theatre-style rows and it wasn't going to be possible to do the activity I had planned for later in the day. In my usual open way, I shared my disgruntlement with the participants, and said what a shame it was that the venue wasn't suitable for what I had intended. During the afternoon, at the point where we would have done the activity, I once again mentioned that we weren't going to be able to, but put a substitute activity in its place which covered many of the areas the first one would have done, so the participants' learning was still able to happen.

What I had not anticipated was that over half the evaluations pointed out that the venue was unsuitable and that it was a shame we had not been able to do the planned activity. By sharing my own dissatisfaction with the participants, I had raised their dissatisfaction and had then received more negative evaluations, even though the changes I had made on the day meant that they had had an equally positive learning experience.

How did I deal with it? By the time I had the evaluations, it was too late to put the situation right. I chose not to further discuss the topic, as I felt that they would have then left the session thinking about what they perceived as the negative aspects of the day. Instead, I focused on what had gone well, the positive aspects of the day and particularly the enthusiasm and participation of the people present, to ensure they left with positive messages.

What did I learn? On reflection, I was able to think about the fact that the workshop participants would never have known about my initial plans for the afternoon activity, and by telling them that they would not be able to do what I had planned, they became dissatisfied. My job as a facilitator means that I am responsible for the process that I take people through, but they don't know what that process is going to be in advance. Now, when I run sessions, I keep in mind that as a facilitator I have no right to pass on my own dissatisfaction to them. I keep to the timings and make sure the participants obtain their stated outcomes, but keep to myself what the detailed programme is, or what it should have been if I have changed it. This way, people have a positive experience, learn what they have come to learn and go away very satisfied with the session.

You can never overplan

I was running a workshop for someone I had never previously met – we had liaised by phone and by email, and as usual I had provided my requirements of the room being laid out with a semi-circle of chairs and what equipment I needed. The workshop was being held in a hotel, in a conference room named the Billiard Room. You may already have guessed where this story is leading – I never thought that the billiard room might actually be filled with an enormous billiard table! The table was of course covered with boarding and tablecloths, and had chairs all around the edge, an environment that was definitely not conducive to learning and interaction.

How did I deal with it? I asked for another room, but all the other conference rooms were booked and I had no choice but to use the allocated room. Fortunately it was a small workshop of less than 10 people, so we re-grouped in the very minimal space at one end of the room for the main sessions, and people were able to work in twos and three around the edges of the billiard table when we needed to do the practical activities.

What did I learn? That even though I had specified my requirements, I had not checked that they were actually going to be possible to achieve, and had not asked for confirmation. I also learned to be as specific as possible, and to be alert to the fact that if liaising through a third party (eg through the workshop organiser to the hotel) messages can be lost, so I now state my requirements at the workshop booking stage and check that the venue will be able to provide what I need.

Trust the process

Early in our empowerment work, we were conducting a research study using the programme 'Empowerment, A Personal Path to Self-Care'. One of the activities was designed to teach the problem-solving process. During this activity, one participant is asked to identify a problem and the whole group then brainstorms possible solutions.

I was facilitating this session and in my preparations, I thought about potential issues participants would raise. I made the assumption that the group would choose a behaviour to discuss such as difficulty losing weight, sticking with a meal plan or exercising. I also generated a list of ideas for these issues based on strategies that other patients had successfully used or I had read about. I felt very well prepared to both lead and contribute to the discussion.

Imagine my surprise when I asked for a volunteer for the group to identify a problem they would like help solving, and a middle-aged gentleman proposed "my wife is not supportive of my diabetes management efforts". I panicked. In my efforts to divert the conversation into an area about which I felt more confident, I asked the group what they thought of this topic. They thought it was great. I was stuck.

How did I deal with it? I took a deep breath, and wrote down the problem and asked for ideas. I expected silence, but instead there was an immediate and lively discussion. They generated a long list of ideas from their experiences in dealing with this issue. After the brainstorming activity, I asked the participant who had first identified this as an issue what he thought of the ideas. He picked one to try. The following week we started the session by hearing about how he had used this idea and how well it had gone. By the end of the programme, his blood glucose levels had considerably improved.

What did I learn? Trust your participants and the process. All of my brilliant ideas related to diet or exercise would not have helped this man better manage his diabetes. When you join rather than lead patients in their diabetes journey, great things happen.

Respect your participants

I am committed to creating an active and collaborative environment in group sessions, and like to create small groups throughout the session, using different methods. One favourite method is by using 'happy families' cards. Each participant receives a card with a member of a family on it, and then meets up with the rest of their 'family' to form a group. I often say "you don't have to take on the role of the family member, it's just to form you into a group!" which creates a laugh and makes sure that people understand the purpose.

I recently bought a new set of happy families cards, from a well-known high street children's store. They had more up to date names and were brighter and much larger than my previous more 'traditional' pack and so I was delighted with them. I used them on my very next workshop, selecting a few sets of families at random from the pack. I distributed the cards, explaining how pleased I was with them. Imagine my surprise when someone came up to me as the groups were forming and said "you didn't have to be so personal you know!"

The person had received the card 'Mr Jumbo, the pilot'. The person was quite overweight, and unbeknown to me, was extremely sensitive about this at that particular time because their family had recently been very unkind to them about it. Being dealt this card had made them remember this and it felt very personal indeed.

How did I deal with it? I quickly reassured the person that the choice of cards was not personal at all, but was simply a way of mixing people up into different groups to work with during the day. Whilst this gave him an explanation, I was aware that he still felt offended by the action I had taken.

What did I learn? It reminded me that it is crucial to select ways of getting people into groups that are as neutral as possible and do not have an obvious personal context. It is also important to state in advance that the purpose of the exercise is to mix people up to work with others, to pre-empt any reactions. I had been so pleased with the look of my cards that I forgot to check if there were new family names that might appear critical and how this might appear to participants.

Conclusion

Group education sessions are extremely useful and enjoyable for a range of healthcare purposes. Apart from being an efficient use of time for the leader and the participants, they create effective and enjoyable learning environments. However, as you have seen, their success depends a great deal on how well they are planned, the care taken in their preparation and the skills the facilitator uses during delivery of the sessions.

This book has taken you through the entire process and brought to life all the separate elements that will enable you to create successful learning in groups. Group based education also gives your participants the fantastic additional benefit of 'meeting, sharing and comparing' with others in a similar situation, which enables learning to last well beyond the group sessions themselves.

We hope the contents of this book have given you new knowledge, new ideas and most important of all, new inspiration for giving your participants the group experience they deserve!

Further Reading

If this book has stimulated you to learn even more about group education and facilitation skills, there are a number of other publications that could give you information. Using the Internet will bring you a massive number of references, so to make it easier we have picked a few titles from different perspectives and academic standards. All are easily available from publishers and retail outlets. We hope they're useful to you!

Elwyn G, Greenhalgh T, Macfarlane F (2004). Groups: a guide to small group work in healthcare, management, education and research. Oxon. Radcliffe.

Detailed, theoretical and practical, and includes examples from the authors' own experiences.

Ramsden P (2005). Learning to teach in Higher Education. Oxon. Routledge Farmer.

A detailed academic text with plenty of references to research studies and contemporary educational debate, but still easy to read and inspiring.

Rogers, J (2001). Adults Learning. Buckingham. Open University Press.

A general and often lighthearted, but informative, guide to helping adults to learn in many different settings, including evening classes and further and higher education.

Printed in Great Britain by
Amazon.co.uk, Ltd.,
Marston Gate.